# The Butterfly Book

## Susan Acker

CELESTIAL ARTS
MILLBRAE, CALIFORNIA

First Printing, March 1975
Made in the United States of America

**Library of Congress Cataloging in Publication Data**

Acker, Susan, 1946—
        The butterfly book.

        1. Butterflies. 2. Insects--Metamorphosis.
I.   Title.
QL544.A28        595.7'89        74-25834
ISBN 0-89087-005-5

# The Butterfly Book

Warm in the dawn sun, she pauses for a brief moment,
a dancing sunbeam, a butterfly.
Light and energy take the shape of
fragile, color-splashed wings.
Even at rest, her small body still flutters gently,
a delicate balance of motion and repose,
captive energy,
and more,
a symbol of the spirit,
the soul.

Scents of the earth rise on warm air currents,
drifting up in a lazy climb toward the sun.
New spring grasses, green and bright,
sparkle with lingering dew.
New growth and green color and crisp odor
reach toward the Butterfly in a soft flood.
All her senses tingle with a delicious excitement.
Wings flex rhythmically, absorbing energy,
shimmering in the bath of golden rays and green reflections.
Their colors grow even brighter.
This is a creature of light,
a symphony of swift and fleeting color.

She pauses for an instant, attracted to a red bloom.
With a slight flutter of wings,
she is resting on the broad petals.
Everywhere is soft texture and sweet fragrance.
The Butterfly tastes with each footstep,
searches with both antennae, and
follows the scent trail deep into the flower.
Down toward the treasure within,
the long spiral tongue unrolls and sips drops of nectar.

"I am like this flower.
I am sweet as it is sweet.
Together we share color and a love
of light and life."


The Butterfly shares much more.
It is bound up with the flower in
Life's mystery and miracle of creation.
As it draws in the spiral straw of its tongue,
a light dusting of pollen
clings to antennae and wings and feet.
On another visit to another flower,
the pollen is brushed off again.
Here it will shape the beginnings of new life—
the beginning of a seed.
And the seeds of love are carried
from one flower to another.
Butterfly and flower are partners in creation.

Gossamer membranes are thatched
with a covering of tiny scales.
One dusty shingle overlaps another.
Its surface is a pattern of ripples and
light-flashing ridges that blend with a color of its own.
Four wings, colorful mosaics,
perfect in their symmetry.
They lift the Butterfly's body and pull
her forward into the singing wind.
What a magic sound must surround her.
Our senses catch the flashing color of those wings,
but the music of wind playing
across myriad scales is hers alone.
Is it the music of rustling autumn leaves,
or the song of the breeze in a pine forest,
faint chords on a harp,
or rushing water in a spring brook?
The harmony is hers alone.

The Butterfly discovers that earth
does clutch at the free spirit,
to bind what cannot be bound without destruction.
On one flower, the Butterfly's soft footsteps
are felt by another. A spider lurks below.
Stealth and cunning borne on hairy legs.
Slowly it slips one long limb and then another
over the edge of a petal.
Closer, one leap away.
A flutter of wings and the Butterfly is gone.
She is not separated from Earth,
not entirely a creature of the air.
But, as with the mystery of creation—
the pollination of the flower—
she is partners with the spider too.
Spider and Butterfly find themselves a part of the whole.
Creation and destruction.
Life and death.
Predator and prey.
One cannot exist without the other.
Now a small creature dimly senses
the balance and the harmony.

Not even free flight can separate the
Butterfly from destiny.
These conflicts of Life and Death reach after her,
now gathering around her in a dark cloud.
A shadow passes overhead.
A bird sweeps close.
The Butterfly is tumbled about in the
turbulence of rushing wings.
Nature's conflicts are quickly settled.
This time Earth has armed the Butterfly.
The balance weighs in her favor.
Instinct snaps bright wings open.
For a precious instant the predator is startled.
And the Butterfly escapes.

What does the Butterfly see?
One flower or a thousand?
Her eyes are not simple but compound,
dark flashing diamonds bearing
thousands of tiny facets.
Each facet is a lens resting on a cone.
Each cone is an eye capturing its own share of light.
Delicate nerves, like finely woven threads,
carry the light's message to a tiny brain.
A miracle of mechanics.
How is that message received?
Do a thousand fine connections form one image?
Or do a flood of dazzling light rays
make a colorful mosaic?
We can only look into these glittering prisms
and imagine that we see a thousand bright images
mirrored in them.

The Butterfly understands the spirit of the wind.
It shares her freedom.
To still it is to destroy it.
The mystery of moving air—
it flows in a sudden rush
sweeping her up
then dying away
yet coming again.
A resurrection.
A reassuring happening.
It touches but cannot be touched.
Tangible yet intangible.
An earthy energy generated by the warmth of the sun.
She soars and two free spirits become one.

Crystal sounds of spring are gathered in a pond community.
It wakes to morning warmth.
The dawn chorus of redwing blackbirds
sing from their perches in the marsh,
the tattered brown flags of cattails left from autumn.
Silent, stiff, stooping with age,
they are sentinels guarding young green shoots.
Filling the air is the sharp odor of fresh mint.
Its leaves are crisp with frost crystals
slowing melting in the sun.
The rising sun and the Butterfly
begin the dawn celebration.
New life, warm day, bright spring.
She skims over the sparkling water
and is the spirit of day,
the soul of spring.

The Butterfly now glides into the shadowy silence
of a dark forest.
She is enveloped by the silence, by the darkness.
Nothing moves.
All is cool.
Shapes are blurred and blended in
an unfamiliar gloom.
Trees stand as tall giants in quiet circles,
motionless, yet sharing a kind of energy.
One sunbeam invades this dim world.
The Butterfly gropes upward,
drawn by the thin thread of light.
Up and up she struggles.
The thread grows brighter, broader, until
all is bright at the top.
Here all come together—
Butterfly, silent giants, warm sun.
The strange becomes familiar.
A dark forest is a sun-loving creature.
The giants are stretching upward to
capture their own share of warm energy.
And in the sun, all become one in the struggle.

To sense what is happening in the world around her
the Butterfly is outfitted with a marvel of
sensitive equipment—
eyes for the shape and color of sight,
delicate antennae and feet for feeling and tasting,
but no ears for sampling a world filled with sound.
The hard shell of her thorax catches vibrations,
but what a pity to suppose she cannot hear
the plaintive chirping of fledglings in a nest,
the sawing of cicadas on a warm afternoon,
the rattle of a locust in the sand,
wind playing through meadow grass,
squirrel chatter, jay shrieks, or
the low lonely call of a dove.
Perhaps instead she hears the
soundless things of life,
clouds floating across a blue expanse of sky,
earth baking and cracking in hot sun,
apples growing,
sounds heard by the spirit.

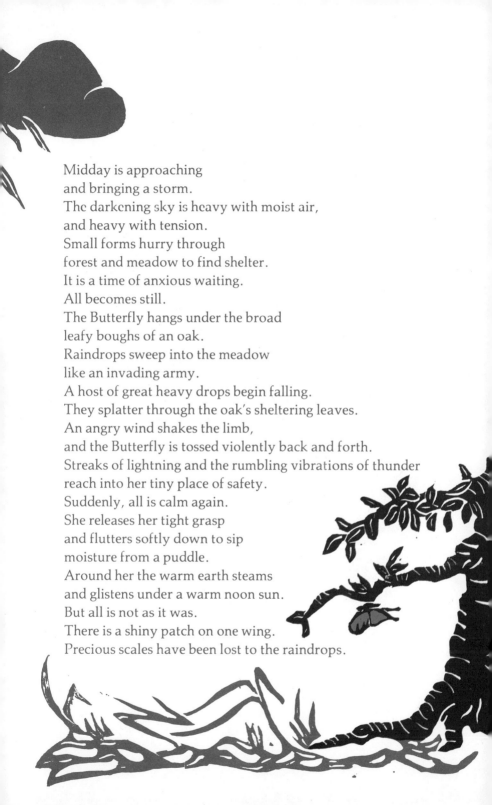

Midday is approaching
and bringing a storm.
The darkening sky is heavy with moist air,
and heavy with tension.
Small forms hurry through
forest and meadow to find shelter.
It is a time of anxious waiting.
All becomes still.
The Butterfly hangs under the broad
leafy boughs of an oak.
Raindrops sweep into the meadow
like an invading army.
A host of great heavy drops begin falling.
They splatter through the oak's sheltering leaves.
An angry wind shakes the limb,
and the Butterfly is tossed violently back and forth.
Streaks of lightning and the rumbling vibrations of thunder
reach into her tiny place of safety.
Suddenly, all is calm again.
She releases her tight grasp
and flutters softly down to sip
moisture from a puddle.
Around her the warm earth steams
and glistens under a warm noon sun.
But all is not as it was.
There is a shiny patch on one wing.
Precious scales have been lost to the raindrops.

The Butterfly let the wind carry her
high over the valley oaks.
Over the hills rolling toward the sea.
She was swept up,
her body buoyant on a cool wave of air.
The spring green of the grasses was becoming
tawny—a hint of the golden fields of summer.
Salty sea air in a fog fall poured over
a high ridge and down into the valleys.
She flew into the mist and over the ridge.
The afternoon sun glowed in golden reflections
on the living surface of the earth.
Golden sea waves blended with
golden waves on the grassy hillsides.
Cool air played over both.
Sea waves swelled toward the coast as
grassy waves rustled and rushed down to the sea.

From the top of the mountain ridge
the Butterfly saw the sun glittering
on ocean waves far below.
Each wave seemed to move in slow motion,
slow rolling swells crashing against the shore.
Each lazy traveler reaching its destination
from faraway ocean depths.
She flew closer until the rhythm
of the breaking waves was lost in
a tumult of sound.
Surf swept into sea caverns,
shattering and filling them with foam.
Waves played through cobbles on the beach.
Fingers of water pushed and prodded until
the stones went rolling and clattering
down to the sea.
The Butterfly was swept up
in the wild roaring of the surf.

The Butterfly retreated to the safety of a small lagoon.
She fluttered at the edge of quiet waters,
as the last of the flood tide drifted slowly in.
A low murmur of water sweeping across the sand
mingled with the wild cries of gulls above.
Sandpipers ran along the tide line like wind-up toys,
imprinting their tiny footprints on the
winding ribbons of wet sand.
Alighting on a rough piece of driftwood,
she watched the tide creeping in,
filling the tracks of the birds,
swirling into ripple marks on the mud.
The tide, symbol of the energy of moving water,
the great living ocean taking long breaths,
symbol of the inevitable.
The tide was turning,
beginning to ebb,
as the Butterfly's life would soon ebb away.

A sea breeze laden with salt spray
lifted the Butterfly back to the forest.
In the dense shade of the quiet giants,
she rested.
She bathed in the balsam fragrance.
A shaft of sunlight made a golden pool
in the center of the ancient cathedral.
Two small birds broke the silence,
all happy dash and color.
They led the Butterfly over a forest floor
clothed in an enchanting cloak of fern and mushroom,
and wildflowers straining for a bit of sun.
A maze of little trails met at a cool stream bank.
She stopped to share it with the others.

In the forest, the Butterfly found truth
mixed with deception in the animal world around her.
She herself resembled a flying flower.
Others were also masters of disguise.
Here were twigs that walked,
thorns that climbed trees,
gentle moths whose coloring mimicked a wasp.
Imitation in Nature is more than mere chance—
it is a matter of survival.
A brooding pheasant hen has feathers which seem
like the fleeting shadows of her nesting ground.
A butterfly with pink spots on its transparent wings
looks like small petals floating down to earth.
Another shows bright eye spots on its wings to
startle birds who jump back as if stung.
A frightened caterpiller inflates and,
flashing eye spots on its back,
it rears and threatens like a serpent.
The breast of a praying mantis is a petal-shaped
bouquet of delicate lavender—
she turns it sunward to wait
for small flower-loving insects—
a diabolical flower trap.
Disguise, imitation, deception, concealment.
The Butterfly rests on a twig and
folds her wings over her back until
all bright color
disappears.

A long glide brings the Butterfly
down beside an ant colony.
A trail of shiny black bodies catches her eye.
It flows out of a dark mound of earth
and stretches endlessly into the meadow grasses.
There is a sudden break in the procession.
One ant pauses.
It lifts a tiny clawed foot
and cleans one antennae with a feathery comb.
A fellow worker rushes blindly into it from behind.
The other, carrying a seed nearly twice its size,
puts the burden down.
The two reach toward each other and
in a mysterious ceremony,
touch and tap antennae.
Then both hurry on their way.
What was said between them?
How does each know his place,
his duty,
his part in the ant order of things?
Is it a predestined world of no choice?
But something was said.
The Butterfly glides on.

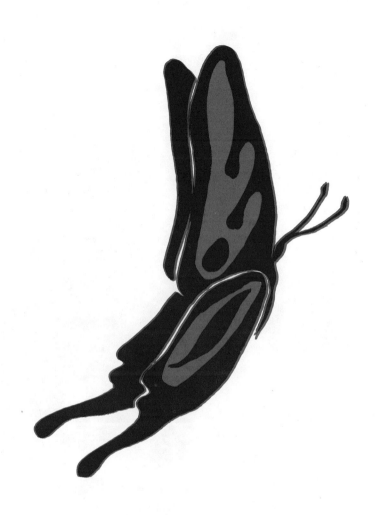

Was she drawn to the Butterfly Tree
by accident,
or because of its fragrance,
or the scent of a thousand other butterflies?
Or is there some mysterious strand of memory
locked secretly within her,
a gift of memory from ancient ancestors who
also flocked to the tree
on warm sunny days long past.
She joins the others for a time,
clinging motionless,
wings tightly folded,
clothing the branches of the tree
with colorfully sparkling leaves.
Those already present give a quick
flutter of their wings in welcome,
and the tree dances with twinkling light.
There is a rustling sound.
A cloud of butterflies swirl softly
upward into blue skies
toward the sun.

The shape of life around the Butterfly is circular.
A magic wheel of
comings and goings,
give and take,
predator and prey,
producer and consumer,
birth and death.
The Butterfly is part of a community of living things.
A community bound, each to another, in countless ways.
A community with form and pattern and rhythm.
Food-gathering, resting, love-making, home-making.
A dynamic community ruled by
the restless forces of nature—
day and night,
drought and flood,
icy cold and burning heat.
In the struggle for existence,
the Butterfly joins the rest,
one thread in the web of life,
webbed with a thousand mysteries.

The life of the Butterfly is a drama of four acts.
Act I — the egg.
Under a leaf hangs a small cluster of eggs.
Painted dew drops.
The ancient ones believed the dew
hardened in the heat of the sun to
form these tiny jewels.
There is a fragile world within.
Here the beginnings of life are infinitely small,
but the promise is grand.
Inside is locked the key to
the transformation of life.
One living creature, the caterpillar,
will give up its life to another, the butterfly.
Inside each egg, one cell divides, becoming two.
Two become four, then eight, sixteen . . .
a thousand cells.
Some form the living, working tissues of the caterpillar,
but others sleep.
The caterpillar will carry them into the next life.
And what call will awaken these sleeping ones
to become the Butterfly's shimmering wings?

Act II begins.
It is morning.
Small, shiny heads appear,
black, huge compared to their slim bodies.
All emerge slowly, simultaneously.
What signal is given?
All hungrily nibble their egg cylinders until
they burst through,
tearing back a tiny lid to escape.
The common cradle is left a group of yawning goblets.
But only for a moment,
because all turn, each fragile bit of life,
consuming its small egg shell.
And with this first meal finished,
they roam toward the great green horizon.

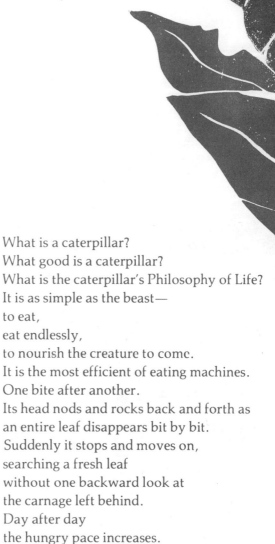

What is a caterpillar?
What good is a caterpillar?
What is the caterpillar's Philosophy of Life?
It is as simple as the beast—
to eat,
eat endlessly,
to nourish the creature to come.
It is the most efficient of eating machines.
One bite after another.
Its head nods and rocks back and forth as
an entire leaf disappears bit by bit.
Suddenly it stops and moves on,
searching a fresh leaf
without one backward look at
the carnage left behind.
Day after day
the hungry pace increases.
Food must be gathered
and stored away within
the fat green contours of its body.
It is ravenous as if it knows
the time of fasting is ahead.

"Catepelose"—the hairy cat.
Its body moves in a series of rippling waves.
Each wave begins near the tail and runs to the head.
Two thousand tiny muscles contract
one after another
until the long elastic body
has moved a fraction of an inch.
Its odd legs are for gripping not walking—
fat claspers at the tail,
four pairs of pads supporting its middle,
six true legs, small hard hooks, forward.
Smooth pale-green skin covers
a body that is supple but not sinewy.
The caterpillar is a clumsy acrobat.
It weighs down a leaf,
and as the leaf drops,
rides it down,
slips off the edge
and dangles in mid-air.
True legs and jaws catch hold while
the hind end wildly hooks up.
Fat pads pinch at thin air until
they find the tip of the leaf,
and greedy jaws continue their work.

Not all of the caterpillars survived.
For even such a simple,
single-minded existence,
threats are everywhere,
right from the beginning.
One of the eggs was eaten by an earwig.
This pale little insect
with the strange pincers on its tail
gobbled up the egg before it hatched.
Another egg was destroyed by a wasp who
pierced the shell and laid one of her own eggs inside.
Several eggs were infertile so that
Act I of the drama never had a chance to begin.
Among the growing caterpillars,
three were snatched from their leaves by hungry birds.
One was captured in the lightning-quick
death-grip of a praying mantis.
And one very fat caterpillar slipped from a leaf
and fell to the ground like an over-ripe fruit.
It wandered blindly about,
unable to find its own food plant
and died alone in the tall grasses.

In Act II are several strange scenes.
The caterpillar crawls out of its own skin!
As it grows, its skin stretches,
elastic to a point,
stretching until it can be stretched no further.
When this time comes, the greedy feasting stops.
Fluid seeps between the tight old skin
and the young new skin growing below it.
Old skin is dissolved.
The caterpillar twists its body.
Muscles flow in little ripples.
Its head arches in the quiet struggle.
Hours pass.
The old skin splits along its back,
and the caterpillar steps out,
dressed in bright new green.
The worn remnant left behind
is only a shell of shiny head and feet
tied together by a bit of shrunken skin.
Greedy to the end, as with the eggshell of its birth,
the caterpillar turns and eats the old skin.
Five times the caterpillar struggles from old to new.
And on the fifth time,
it vanishes forever.

Act III comes quickly.
One day the caterpillar turns away from the feast.
It wanders and climbs higher.
Overpowering restlessness.
Head arching, it sways and searches space.
Under one broad leaf it pauses.
The segments of its body contract until
it becomes a writhing green drop.
Skin splits behind its head along its back.
Convulsions continue until for the last time
the empty skin falls away.
The caterpillar has disappeared.
In its place is the chrysalis,
a being neither caterpillar nor butterfly,
a strange sarcophagus shrouding a tiny spark of life.
It is as still as death,
yet inside the locked room,
sleeping cells are awakening and
the cells of the caterpillar regroup.
Outwardly, the chrysalis seems to sleep out this
period of transition between child and adult,
limbo between one life and the next.
It joins caterpillar to butterfly and
it will be joining earth to heaven.

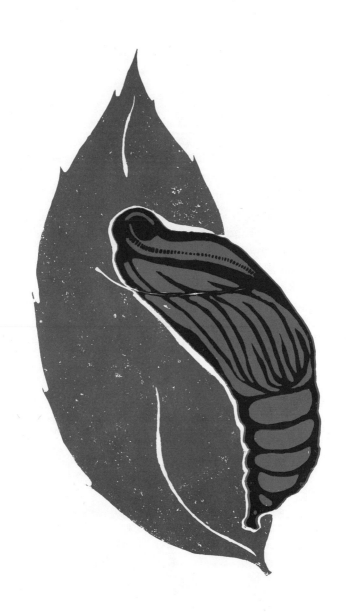

In its dark helplessness
the chrysalis hangs from a silk pad at its tail
and is supported by a silken lifeline slipped
under its shoulders.
Only the waxy green of the caterpillar remains,
until even that last reminder fades to deep gray.
Silvery spots, like so many mirrors,
make the chrysalis a living chandelier,
catching and reflecting flashing bits of sunlight.
On its surface is etched the outline of
the butterfly folded tightly within—
faint tracery of antennae and veined wings.
It is cool, quiet, perfect design.

Act IV
The glorious renaissance is about to begin.
The shell of the chrysalis is glistening,
transparent,
dry.
From deep within comes a shudder.
The tiny cornucopia bursts open,
and the Butterfly forces its way out.
Free now, it clings to the dry shell
and hangs motionless for a long time
as if gathering strength.
In less than a second its body
is twice as large as the empty case.
Soft, floppy, the wings hang down,
a dark crumpled mass of wrinkles.
Slowly they expand.
Their veins fill and harden as strengthening
fluid is pumped from the heart.
The two halves of the long tongue coil and uncoil,
locking themselves together to form a sucking tube.
Finally the wings can open and shut,
now rich in color and
strong enough to carry the Butterfly away
on the first dawn breeze.

The Butterfly is the final product
of this marvelous life cycle.
The greedy caterpillar fulfilled its purpose—
to store up life-giving tissue,
the raw materials,
to create the body of the Butterfly.
Then it gave up its life,
never to see the beauty of the creature to follow,
slipping quietly away in
the chrysalis' locked room.
Now the Butterfly will continue
carrying that thread of life full circle.
She will mate and lay the eggs
that will close the circle.

She savors a delicious afternoon sun.
Her life is drawing near its climax,
a drama nearing a swift but glorious curtain.
The quality of the sunlight on that afternoon
was especially bright and sweet.
It flooded the meadow with a golden haze.
Delicate threads of spider webs
were caught up in the light
and glistened as they never had before.
The colors of the flowers grew deeper.
The earth hummed with warm energy.

At an unfamiliar edge of the meadow
she met another butterfly,
a butterfly who stirred her small being
with a new sense of excitement.
His wings pumped slowly up and down.
He was guarding a tiny patch of earth,
his territory.
Alert, aggressive, antennae thrust stiffly out,
he darted toward the intruder,
whirling upward,
spinning round and round,
a violent greeting that ended as quickly as it began.
All menacing movement stopped as
he alighted and waited
silently.

Moments passed.
With a sound like the quick rustle of a paper fan,
the Other rushed toward her.
Smooth glides and fluttering stops,
they circled each other in a stately minuet.
She spread her wings wide,
spiralling upward toward the sun.
He followed.
A delicious fragrance surrounded him,
the faint perfume of faraway honeysuckle.
It drew her close.
Together they made a song of wings and sun,
bright sparks of burning gold,
the essence of joy.

And then she was alone,
but complete, ,
a life filled and close to fulfillment.
Within her there stirred a sense of purpose,
a very heavy sense of purpose,
for she was burdened with eggs.
They had been slowly developing since
the moment she stepped from the chrysalis,
and now, rich with life themselves,
they were ready to begin the drama anew.
Across the meadow,
over a dozen meadows,
she carefully choose just the right leaves,
and attached a bright drop of new life
on each green cradle.

The evening of the long day came slowly.
On a dry twig of an oak,
on the edge of the meadow where she was born,
the Butterfly rested in the gathering dusk.
Evening mists drew gently about her.
She could see the ghost moths in the grass.
Hundreds, dimly visible in their whiteness.
They danced a pale and rhythmic love dance
in the wide silent night.
Gone was the fire and sun of her own dance,
but it was a magic time,
for the dark heaven twinkled with
a thousand faraway suns and
their sparks fell on the pale dancing ghosts below.
As the shadows piled up silently under the oak,
the Butterfly sailed across the meadow a last time.
The vibrant color of her wings
and of her mood is spent.
She is a fragile faded flower.
Wings frayed and ragged.
Patches of scales worn away.
She seems clad in a threadbare coat.
A body once rounded with eggs
is now thin and shriveled.
Laboring wings sweep her low over the grass.
She hangs in the air,
swinging like an uneven pendulum
sinking slowly to rest.

For such a brief time,
the Butterfly had been caught up in the whirlpool of life,
a whirlpool charged with the energy of sunlight,
whirling about her and within her.
Her life was predestined to be quick and full,
patterned to pass through a miracle of rebirth,
which no other creature on earth shares with her.
From caterpillar to chrysalis she carried inside
that very special vital spark.
Her emergence is a living sign,
a symbol
to see,
to understand,
and to find within ourselves.

Sounds of a day pass into those of a night.
Twilight sharpened sound.
Wind flows among the grasses
as if it were on some sad search.
The Butterfly lies with wings tightly folded
over her back against the cold night air.
She was so simple a form of energy,
a very thin but pure thread
woven into a tiny bit of down and feathers.
Into a world of Life so encumbered
with meaningless decorations that
it is easily lost and forgotten,
the Butterfly carries simple truth.
The true nature of life.
Now she sleeps.

# CELESTIAL ARTS BOOK LIST

LOVE IS AN ATTITUDE, poetry and photographs by Walter Rinder.
   03-0 Paper @ $3.95        04-9 Cloth @ $7.95

THIS TIME CALLED LIFE, poetry and photographs by Walter Rinder.
   05-7 Paper @ $3.95        06-5 Cloth @ $7.95

SPECTRUM OF LOVE, poetry by Walter Rinder with David Mitchell art.
   19-7 Paper @ $2.95        20-0 Cloth @ $7.95

FOLLOW YOUR HEART, poetry by Walter Rinder with Richard Davis art.
   39-1 Paper @ $2.95

THE HUMANNESS OF YOU, Vol. 1, art and philosophy by Walter Rinder.
   47-2 Paper @ $2.95

THE HUMANNESS OF YOU, Vol. 2, art and philosophy by Walter Rinder.
   54-5 Paper @ $2.95

VISIONS OF YOU, poetry by George Betts and photography by Robert Scales.
   07-3 Paper @ $3.95

MY GIFT TO YOU, poetry by George Betts and photography by Robert Scales.
   15-4 Paper @ $3.95

YOU & I, poetry and photography by Leonard Nimoy.
   26-X Paper @ $3.95        27-8 Cloth @ $7.95

WILL I THINK OF YOU?, poetry and photography by Leonard Nimoy.
   70-7 Paper @ $3.95

SPEAK THEN OF LOVE, poetry by Andrew Oerke with Asian art.
   29-4 Paper @ $3.95

I AM, concepts of awareness in poetic form by Michael Grinder with color art.
   25-1 Paper @ $2.95

GAMES STUDENTS PLAY, transactional analysis in schools by Ken Ernst.
   16-2 Paper @ $3.95        17-0 Cloth @ $7.95

GUIDE FOR SINGLE PARENTS, transactional analysis by Kathryn Hallett.
   55-3 Paper @ $3.95        64-2 Cloth @ $7.95

PASSIONATE MIND, guidance and understanding by Joel Kramer.
   63-4 Paper @ $3.95

SENSIBLE BOOK, understanding children's senses by Barbara Polland.
   53-7 Paper @ $3.95

THIS TIMELESS MOMENT, Aldous Huxley's life by Laura Huxley.
   22-5 Paper @ $4.95

HEALING MIND, explains the healing powers of the mind by Dr. Irving Oyle.
   80-4 Paper @ $4.95

HOW TO BE SOMEBODY, a guide for personal growth by Yetta Bernhard.
   20-9 Paper @ $4.95

CREATIVE SURVIVAL, the problems of single mothers by Persia Woolley.
   17-9 Paper @ $4.95

FAT LIBERATION, the awareness technique to losing weight by Alan Dolit.
   03-9 Paper @ $3.95

ALPHA BRAIN WAVES, explanation of same by D. Boxerman and A. Spilken.
   16-0 Paper @ $4.95

INWARD JOURNEY, art as therapy by Margaret Keyes.
   81-2 Paper @ $4.95

GOD, poetic visions of the abstract by Alan Watts.
   75-8 Paper @ $3.95

Write for a free catalog to:
CELESTIAL ARTS   231 Adrian Road   Millbrae, California 94030